Garfield

GETS A LIFE

BY: JIM DAVIS

RAVETTE BOOKS

TOING I TOING

141, 142, 143, 144,... GARFIELD, DID YOU KNOW THE BEDROOM CEILING HAS 144 TILES

THE LIVING ROOM HAS 214

I'M BORED

WHY DON'T YOU ORGANIZE YOUR SOCK DRAWER?

I'D ORGANIZE MY SOCK DRAWER, BUT I JUST ORGANIZED IT LAST NIGHT

I'LL BE THE JUDGE OF THAT

WHOA, I'M IMPRESSED. ALL NICELY TUCKED AND SORTED BY COLOUR AND SIZE

THESE ARE THE WINTER SOCKS. THE SUMMER ONES ARE IN THE OTHER DRAWER

HERE WE HAVE YOUR NATURAL FIBRE SOCKS, HERE'S YOUR MAN-MADE FIBRE SOCKS, AND OF COURSE, HERE YOU'VE GOT YOUR BLENDS

YOU KNOW WHAT, GARFIELD?

YOU NEED A LIFE

I NEED A LIFE

I FORGOT I HAD THIS BOOK. HEY, THIS CHAPTER ON GETTING DATES IS JUST THE TICKET

GREAT. READ IT AND GIVE ME A FULL REPORT. THE SOONER YOU GET HAPPY WITH YOUR LIFE, THE SOONER I CAN GET BACK TO MINE

HUMANS...NEVER SATISFIED... IF ONLY THEY'D LEARN TO BE CONTENT WITH THE SIMPLE THINGS IN LIFE... LIKE LASAGNA...

A GOOD NAP...

FAMILY...

DOG BREATH PEE-YEW!

HUH?

IT SAYS HERE, A SINGLES CLUB IS JUST THE TICKET

...FOR A HAPPENIN' GUY LIKE ME

DID YOU HEAR THAT, GARFIELD? SHE WANTS TO DANCE WITH ME

IT'S A MIRACLE

COME, MY DEAR, LET'S CUT A RUG

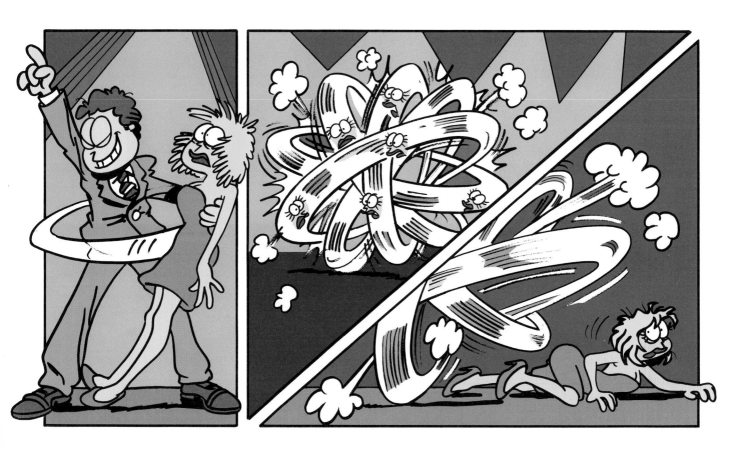

MAYBE I OUGHTA JUST FORGET ABOUT MEETING ANYONE...EVER. MAYBE I'LL BECOME A NUN

AS LONG AS IT GETS YOU OUT OF THE HOUSE

HI THERE

TAKE A HIKE

NO THANKS, I JUST TOOK ONE

STRIKE TWO

AND NOW, THIS WORD FROM OUR SPONSOR

FRIENDS...

ARE YOU LONELY?

BORED? A LOSER? IS YOUR IDEA OF A FUN SATURDAY NIGHT SITTING AT HOME WATCHING TV

...WITH YOUR CAT?

PPPTTT!

ARE YOU SO BORING THAT YOU COULD MAKE CHEESE YAWN?

ARE YOU SO OUT OF TOUCH THAT YOU THINK DISCO IS STILL "IN"?

HAVE YOU EVER PASSED THE TIME BY COUNTING CEILING TILES?

COMPARED TO YOU DOES A SLUG SEEM HYPERACTIVE?

WELL FRIEND, IF THIS IS YOU, CHEER UP! THERE IS HELP FOR YOU AT THE...

THAT'S RIGHT. AT "LORENZO'S SCHOOL FOR THE PERSONALITY IMPAIRED" WE CAN SHOW YOU HOW TO GET A LIFE

WE CAN TAKE EVEN THE MOST HUMDRUM, UNINTERESTING, AND TIRESOME BORE

BEFORE

...AND TURN HIM INTO SOMEONE VITAL, ENERGETIC, AND SELF-ASSURED

AFTER

WE'LL SHOW YOU HOW TO MAKE FRIENDS.

HOW TO DO IMPRESSIONS.

HOW TO HAVE FUN

AT 'LORENZO'S SCHOOL FOR THE PERSONALITY IMPAIRED' WE'VE GOT A PROVEN TRACK RECORD

I WONDER IF THEY COULD HELP ME?

REMEMBER FRIENDS, OUR MOTTO IS...

"IF YOU CAN GET A PULSE,

...YOU CAN GET A LIFE."

MAYBE THEY'LL TAKE YOU ANYWAY

HOW DO YOU DO? MY NAME IS LORENZO

WHAT IS YOUR NAME?

JON, JON ARBUCKLE

AND THIS IS MY...ER...ARE YOU THE LORENZO IN THE COMMERCIAL?

IN PERSON

NOW, "HOW MIGHT I DO THAT?" YOU MIGHT ASK

YOU DO THAT BY WALKING RIGHT UP TO THEM...

LOOK THEM RIGHT IN THE...

EYE...

GIVING THEM A FIRM HANDSHAKE...

IN ALL MODESTY, I MUST CONFESS, IN SOME CIRCLES...

I AM CONSIDERED A FASHION PLATE, IF YOU WILL

HEE-HEE   HEE

HEE

HEE   HEE

LET ME SHARE A FEW OF MY FASHION SECRETS WITH YOU

L

LOOK AND LEARN

NOTHING IMPRESSES PEOPLE MORE THAN WHEN YOU SPEAK IN A FOREIGN LANGUAGE

BUT YOU DON'T REALLY HAVE TO LEARN A LANGUAGE...

IF YOU CAN SOUND LIKE YOU SPEAK IT

PEOPLE ARE REALLY IMPRESSED IF YOU CAN SPEAK FRENCH OR IF YOU CAN SOUND FRENCH

FOR EXAMPLE, "JE PARLE EN FRANCAIS"

OOOOHHHH!

LE IMPRESSIVE, NO?

IT'S BEEN A WONDERFUL DAY, JON. CLASS WAS GREAT AND DINNER WAS FUN

BUT MOST OF ALL I'VE REALLY ENJOYED TALKING TO YOU

UNTIL I MET YOU, I THOUGHT I WAS THE ONLY PERSON IN THE WORLD TO GET MY TONGUE CAUGHT IN AN ELEVATOR DOOR

I'VE REALLY ENJOYED TALKING TO YOU TOO, MONA, AND WE DIDN'T HAVE TO SPEAK FRENCH

WHAT?

THINK ABOUT IT

WE HAD A WONDERFUL EVENING WITHOUT HAVING TO RELY ON ANYTHING WE LEARNED IN CLASS TODAY

THUV!

OH NO! POOR JON! HE DOESN'T KNOW WHAT HE'S GETTING INTO. I MUST STOP HIM BEFORE HE MULTIPLIES!

THEN IN MY SENIOR YEAR... WHA?!!

GARFIELD?! WHAT ARE YOU DOING?

JON, YOU DON'T KNOW WHAT YOU'RE DOING

WHAT A SWEET CAT

DON'T LISTEN TO HER, JON! SHE'S TRYING TO GET TO YOU THROUGH ME!

WOULD YOU LIKE ME TO SCRATCH BEHIND YOUR EARS?

OH! THAT'S GOOD

SHE'S VERY GOOD, JON. ONCE SHE HAS ME IN HER CLUTCHES SHE'LL...

PERHAPS JUST A LITTLE BIT BEHIND THIS EAR

JON, LISTEN CAREFULLY. THIS IS ALL A...

JUST A LITTLE LOWER, PLEASE... THIS IS ALL A SINISTER PLOT TO GET YOU TO...OH YES! NOW...

THERE'S SOMETHING TO BE SAID FOR SENIORITY

CAN WE STILL SEE EACH OTHER SOMETIME, JON?

I'D LIKE THAT

NOT WITHOUT A CHAPERON. JON'S MORE THAN A FRIEND TO ME... HE'S MY MEAL TICKET

COME ON. I'LL TAKE YOU HOME

HANG ON! WAIT FOR ME!